The Collection
2024

compiled by John Field

EXPRESS NEWSPAPERS

 CASSELL

First published in Great Britain in 2023 by Cassell,
a division of Octopus Publishing Group Ltd, Carmelite House,
50 Victoria Embankment, London EC4Y 0DZ
www.octopusbooks.co.uk

An Hachette UK Company
www.hachette.co.uk

British Cartoon Archive

Cartoons supplied by British Cartoon Archive
Cartoons compiled by John Field

ISBN 978 1 78840 357 3

A CIP catalogue record for this book is available from the British Library.

Printed and bound in China

10 9 8 7 6 5 4 3 2 1

MIX
Paper | Supporting
responsible forestry
FSC® C008047

Contents

Giles & Gatherings 7

Village Fetes & Activities 10

At School 26

Sporting Crowds 49

Parties 79

At the Pub 98

At Church 125

Strikes & Demonstrations 147

British Cartoon Archive 160

Daily Express, 24 December 1981

Giles & Gatherings

This year's collection has been chosen to illustrate Giles's skill, and obvious pleasure, in capturing the complexities generated by a collection of people, crowded together in one place. He was a master at showing gatherings with a wide range of individual characters and social groupings and picking out the nuances of each and every one. Sometimes, he would create a situation where a clash between different groups, such as social classes, age groups, political viewpoints and lifestyles, is inevitable. His drawing skills enabled him to give each person an individual appearance and character, even in the most crowded scenes.

Giles's cartoonist's eye was always astute at picking up on events in which many people would gather, and which would provide him ripe opportunities for drawing the full casts of characters for which he became renowned. Over the years he covered a huge number of events and a small selection are showcased here. Village Fetes & Activities are areas rife with clashes and contests among the local community and At School gives the younger (but still equally mischievous) generation a chance to run riot away from the constraints of the family home. Sporting Crowds see people gathering for a common purpose but are not, of course, without their conflict and football hooliganism in particular was something

about which Giles was particularly acerbic (as shown in the cartoon dated 29 November 1962, on page 62). Parties adeptly showcase the merriment, and mishaps, of Giles's characters letting their hair down, while At the Pub is often a more subdued affair (but nonetheless ripe with disagreements between punters). You would expect that, At Church, Giles's characters would be better behaved but that is rarely the case, as you'll see in this selection, while Strikes & Demonstrations shows that the political disquiet we have seen in recent years is often part and parcel of British life.

The cartoon opposite – captioned "Rejoice good Christian men – the group's arrived." – gives us the opportunity to take a deep dive into Giles's mastery at illustrating many different groups at once. It portrays a large Giles family Christmas Eve party, taking place in the family home in 1981. In total 41 people are present – 34 adults and 7 children, with a few animals thrown in for good measure – all crowded together in a room and around its two entrances.

Aside from the Giles family members, the gathering also comprises a range of different groups including a young set, a young professional element, a middle-aged group, a number of more elderly characters and, finally, the entertainers.

8

Starting with the family members, scattered around the room (or not), we see the following: Grandma, engrossed in her study of the latest racing tips, totally ignores the swinging party surrounding her. As usual, her handbag is safely padlocked and chained to her arm and, obviously, a glass of gin, or possibly whisky, is at hand. Father, sitting relaxed on a settee, does not seem too pleased to see the arrival of the entertainment. Mother is very busy, as usual. This time, looking a little harassed, she is keeping the party well-stocked with drink. George, the family's eldest son, not renowned for his social skills, is missing – probably upstairs reading. Vera, George's wife, nursing yet another cold, has a bottle of pills at hand and, as usual, is totally unaware of her distressed son, George Junior, sitting on the settee between his Aunt Ann and Grandfather. George Junior, with his father, George, absent from the party, and Vera, his mother, totally engrossed with her latest cold, is, as usual, left on his own to cope with one of Stinker's persistent unsettling tricks. Ann, the family's eldest daughter, on the settee alongside George Junior, is as composed as ever, with probably her latest beau, bearded and wearing a patterned shirt, alongside her. Her twins, Laurence and Ralph, named after their mother's favourite actors, Sir Laurence Olivier and Sir Ralph Richardson, are out of sight and, as is often the case, engrossed in a joint exercise aimed at creating a disturbance. Carol, the rather quiet second daughter, sitting on the other settee, appears to have a strong link with the professional-looking gentleman beside her and the child on her right is obviously equal to the younger members of the Giles family in their ability to make trouble. Bridget, the youngest daughter, next to her father on the settee, and often portrayed as an observer of the family's antics, is enthralled by all the activity going on around her. Ernie, so often the one taking charge of family affairs, despite his relatively young age, is presiding as the party's impresario and has taken it upon himself to announce the arrival of the party's entertainment, which is not necessarily welcomed by all. Stinker, the next door neighbours' child, sitting on the chair by the curtains and often seen in cahoots with Ernie, is possibly in charge of the programme of events. He is without his camera on this occasion, which is unusual at Giles family events.

Moving to the guests, the Young Set hold the centre stage, with a jumble of teenage boys, wearing a mixture of trainers, jeans, tartan trousers and T-shirts and girls, wearing mainly patterned skirts and dresses. Note the spotty youth, with his young girlfriend, clinging to the edge of the group – not yet really part of the set.

The two obviously professional young men, on a settee, are appropriately dressed with their "sharp" suits and highly-coiffured hairstyles, while the middle-aged men at the party are more casually dressed, perhaps illustrating their world-weary attitudes towards such festivities as Christmas parties.

The older guests are mainly on the edge of the party, including some just outside the door, and most are dressed up for the party, including one elderly gentleman sporting wing collars that pay homage to the Edwardian period. The rather prim older lady near the settee, in her large polka-dot dress, seems to be anticipating the musical interlude with pleasure.

Regarding the musicians, Giles has made them look as if they come from another age all together.

It should be noted that the family's pets are also present at the party, providing an independent set of activities at floor level: Butch, the family's Airedale Terrier, has his frequent look of benign acceptance of the vagaries of living in the Giles household. I am unable to identify the fluffy-looking thing to his left, but suspect it is a female Pomeranian guest he has invited along. Rush, the Border Collie, in his best "alert sheepdog" pose, is obviously concentrating on something – could it be the arrival of the musicians? Or has he got his eye on the fluffy thing? Natalie, the family cat, without a large litter of kittens on this occasion, is slinking around in the bottom right-hand corner of the cartoon, no doubt looking for food.

It should also be noted that Giles could not resist including two of his favourite hidden jokes in this cartoon: Stinker, the neighbours' son is, almost abstractedly, up to his usual pastime of upsetting George Junior, this time using his well-practised "spider on a string" method. Grandma's parrot, Attila the Hun, taking a leaf out of his owner's book and always on the lookout for mischief, is about to cause mayhem by "felling" the family's Christmas tree, as so often happens in Giles's Christmas cartoons.

Finally, it is interesting to note that, at a time when smoking was more prevalent than today, there are only four smokers in the room – two cigars, one pipe and Grandma with her cigarette. Perhaps Giles was ahead of his time in predicting this social change?

John Field

Village Fetes & Activities

The UK applied to join the European Common Market in 1961 but French President Charles de Gaulle vetoed British admission, in 1963 and again in 1967. Note: this cartoon depicts the Suffolk Show, held in Ipswich.

"In the event of joining the Common Market how do you order two warm beers flat as ink in French?"

Daily Express, 7 June 1962

Unreliable summer weather hasn't dampened the spirits of Ernie and the twins who are delighted with their win, though Father is rather less so. Mop-haired neighbour Stinker seems equally pleased with his fete haul.

"You might try and LOOK pleased they've won a little pig."

Sunday Express, 7 August 1966

There had been a mix-up during the crowning ceremony at the Miss England beauty contest the previous day.

"You make the same mistake in the judging as they did with Miss England, boy, and I'll maim you."

Sunday Express, 18 May 1969

A few days before this cartoon appeared, the owner of the Lady Jane boutique in London's Carnaby Street had arranged a window display of six naked women to publicise the opening of the boutique. Unsurprisingly, a crowd gathered and he was arrested for causing an obstruction.

"Nude models may be right for Carnaby Street, Mrs. Barker, but not for the Ladies O.S. Stall, St. Botolph's Jumble Sale."

Sunday Express, 1 June 1969

14 Perhaps not the Anglo–French relationship British prime minister Edward Heath and his French counterpart Georges Pompidou had expected at their summit – aimed at moving UK membership of the EEC closer – in Paris a few weeks earlier.

"Monsieur complains that your Aberdeen Angus has been striking up a kind of relationship with his Champion Charolais."

Daily Express, 3 June 1971

Despite the vicar's views, one could sympathise with the pithy language as the unreliable English weather ruins the fete. June of 1971 was particularly cold, wet and miserable.

"I am aware that a certain magistrate approves of four letter words in our Permissive Society, but I will not have them used in my Parish when referring to the weather, Mr. Matheson."

Sunday Express, 6 June 1971

It's hard to say which has riled the vicar more – Grandma's comment or being poked in the stomach none too gently with her trusty umbrella. The Family Planning Act five years earlier had made contraception more readily available.

"We didn't need Family Planning when we were boys, eh, Vicar?"

Daily Express, 15 August 1972

Both fickle weather and the Summer Olympics in Munich, which ended the following day, conspire to keep people away from the washed-away fete.

"Bad enough them holding their Olympics same time as us."

Sunday Express, 10 September 1972

In 1974, Britain faced a sugar shortage because of a sharp reduction in sugar cane imports, as Caribbean countries began selling their sugar to more lucrative markets. Some shops introduced rationing.

"We will lift up our eyes unto the heavens so that the member of our flock who hath inadvertently nicked the sugar may return it unseen."

Sunday Express, 4 August 1974

Workers at car manufacturer British Leyland's plants engaged in repeated industrial action during the 1970s.

19

"I assure you there is no question of victimisation because you are Leyland workers – it's simply that we have sold out of raffle tickets."

Sunday Express, 4 July 1976

20 Ernie is cannily capitalising on press reports of a poem Prince Philip had written about a Dundee pub, visited as part of the Silver Jubilee trip to Scotland. However, Vera's jumble stall is unlikely to raise quite as much as the sale of the contents of Mentmore Towers, built for the Rothschilds, which were auctioned by Sotheby's in 1977.

"And how are things going at Mentmore?"

Sunday Express, 29 May 1977

Geoff Boycott, one of England's most successful batsmen, had hit his famous 100th first-class century against Australia just a few days earlier – a feat only to be dreamed of by the motley players of Village Gents v Vicar & Flock at this village match.

"Wake up, Boycott – you're in."

Sunday Express, 14 August 1977

22 The Royal Commission on gambling reported in July 1978 that about 94 per cent of the adult population gambled sometimes, spending nearly £8 billion. One-third entered the pools every week, about 10 per cent bet regularly on the horses and dogs and 4 per cent played bingo.

"You realise your 10p raffle ticket to win that contributes to the yearly £8,000,000,000 we squander on gambling."

Sunday Express, 16 July 1978

Mrs Montpelier-Smythe might be peeved by the vicar's indiscreet comment but everyone else, dogs included, silently agrees that the rock cakes are more suited to construction than eating.

"Daddy, I think Mrs. Montpelier-Smythe heard you say, thanks to her rock cakes, building may now commence."

Sunday Express, 15 July 1979

Famous jockey Lester Piggott, no stranger to controversy and run-ins with authority, had been fined for whipping another jockey. Customers at Grandma's homemade wine stall have imbibed enough of her no-doubt heady brews not to care what is happening in the donkey race.

"Patricia! No Lester Piggott tactics, please!"

Sunday Express, 31 May 1981

Grandma's impressive bowling sends Uncle Dennis's stumps flying. At the time, the Marylebone Cricket Club (MCC), celebrating its 200th anniversary, was taking on a "Rest of the World" team at Lord's in a five-day match.

"As it is the MCC Bicentenary you could have let Uncle Dennis score just one run in his own garden."

Sunday Express, 23 August 1987

At School

Arsenal football team were trounced 5–0 in a friendly fixture against Dynamo Moscow in October 1954, the first-ever visit by a British football team to what was then the Soviet Union.

"I trust you're restricting your form's Dynamo tactics to the playing fields, Mr. Wilmot?"

Daily Express, 7 October 1954

The Ministry of Education was reported in January 1959 as saying that British school children were tending to become too fat. The grimly satisfied PE teacher has come with a sure-fire way of getting the boys to shed those pounds. Moto perpetuo, literally "perpetual motion", is a fast piece of music, usually of equal note lengths.

"An hour every day to the speed of Moto Perpetuo will take care of those extra pounds."

Daily Express, 22 January 1959

Chalkie obviously had no truck with the one-day strike that had been called by the National Association of Schoolmasters.

"Chaps, you'll be interested to know that you took yesterday off but Mr. Chalk didn't."

Daily Express, 21 September 1961

Newspapers had reported that Edward Boyle, Minister of Education, had submitted details of salary proposals for teachers to the Burnham Committee, established in 1919 to negotiate teachers' salaries.

"I have a message from Sir Edward Boyle saying he has received a letter from one of my pupils advising that my salary be knocked in half."

Daily Express, 14 March 1963

National Nature Week in 1963 was organised by the Council for Nature with the aim of highlighting the need to preserve wildlife and natural habitats.

"Miss!"

Sunday Express, 19 May 1963

It appears that Chalkie has solved the problem of the teacher shortage reported in the press the previous day by recruiting a pair of heavyweight boxers to assist Miss Mole.

"Smithy – I don't like the look of Miss Mole's auxiliary helpers one little bit."

Daily Express, 22 April 1965

Three days earlier, theatre critic Kenneth Tynan had become the first person to use the F-word on television, in a live broadcast on BBC One.

"That's my Chalkieboy – Man on the TV uses a four-letter word and we all get 400 lines for knowing what it means."

Daily Express, 16 November 1965

Willie might be struggling with the ale but the rest of the class are enjoying their introduction to alcohol, including those unloading barrels with alacrity in the background.

"If Willie can't drink a pint of old ale without getting pickled Willie won't be ready for the hard stuff next term."

Sunday Express, 16 January 1966

The regulation school uniform has been forgotten by all but one over the summer holidays, replaced with the full gamut of Swinging Sixties' fashion from go-go boots and minis to Space-Age dresses.

"Before the new term gets under way we'll have a few minutes' discussion on what happened to the school uniform."

Daily Express, 6 September 1966

This commemoration of the Battle of Hastings, fought on 14 October 1066, has descended into havoc. Chalkie, in the role of King Harold II, has been felled by a prop flail, poorly aimed arrows are raining down on the ambulance and Stinker seems intent on letting down its tyre.

"Alas! Thou didst most verily catch the fair Chalkie a beauty upon his nut."

Daily Express, 11 October 1966

The BBC had rejected Dennis Potter's script for *Cinderella*, conceived as a Christmas special for a series called The Wednesday Play, in which Prince Charming strangles Cinderella at midnight.

"I don't care if Prince Charming does strangle Cinderella on TV – nobody's going to hang the Three Wise Men and split the loot in our school play."

Daily Express, 8 December 1966

One wonders if Larry Willmott, aka Stinker, may be the gentleman in question. The term "sex kitten" was originally used in the 1950s to describe French actress Brigitte Bardot.

37

"Will the gentleman who endowed the new biology mistress with the undesirable term 'Sex Kitten' step out here."

Daily Express, 5 January 1967

In the early 1970s women were increasingly allowed to wear trouser suits in the workplace
but these schoolgirls are evidently not in favour.

"They've sent me home because I'm wearing a trouser suit."

Daily Express, 12 January 1971

Having – appropriately – caused a stink, the inventor makes good his escape.

39

"Hold it right there! Will the brighter pupil inform the less-bright pupils of an antidote to his latest concoction?"

Daily Express, 28 September 1978

With a semi-automatic rifle replacing the more customary shepherd's staff and the role of angel fraught with danger, this nativity play promises to be far from the usual sweet and serene affair.

"Nowhere in our non-violent script does it say: 'Enter poor shepherds armed with Russian 7.62mm SKS carbines.'"

Daily Express, 14 December 1978

"I have a report that some of you undesirables have kidnapped our caretaker because he refuses to strike."

Daily Express, 8 February 1979

42 Understandably, these would-be kings are displeased about being compared to pickled onions. Their work boots and shaved heads mark them out as skinheads, a subculture that had revival in the early 1980s.

"Whoever heard of Three Kings from the East with heads bald as pickled onions, Miss Sinclair?"

Daily Express, 11 December 1980

Autumn of 1983 marked the start of the installation of ground-launched Cruise missiles in bases in Europe, including two in Britain: at RAF Greenham Common and RAF Molesworth.

"He says if he'd been Joseph he'd have retaliated with a couple of Cruise missiles and blown Herod to kingdom come."

Daily Express, 6 December 1983

May Day or Workers' Day, is celebrated on 1 May in many countries as a holiday. It seems the pupils think the UK should be one of them. Since 1978, the May Day Bank Holiday has been marked on the first Monday in May.

"Here comes our instant strike-breaker."

Daily Express, 1 May 1984

The Animal Liberation Front was formed in the UK in the 1970s to take action against animal cruelty.

45

"It's the Animal Liberation Front protesting about donkeys with three people on doing Jersualem to Bethlehem without a break."

Daily Express, 27 November 1984

Chalkie's dreary twig in a vase doesn't make art classes quite as appealing as those apparently enjoyed at Eton.

"Gentlemen, may I introduce you to Chalkie's answer to beautiful nude Russian models like they give 'em at Eton."

Daily Express, 4 March 1986

A headteacher had recently made the news for banning competition in the school.
Non-competitive sports days are, of course, common now.

"I'll do my best not to win, but if I lose I'll knock the stuffing out of you."

Sunday Express, 13 July 1986

Dennis Potter's award-winning, six-part TV series *The Singing Detective* was being broadcast on Sunday evenings at the time. It starred Michael Gambon as a mystery writer hospitalised with psoriasis – from which Potter also suffered – whose mind is slipping into hallucinations.

"This year's play has nothing that a couple of scenes from *The Singing Dectective* couldn't improve."

Daily Express, 9 December 1986

Sporting Crowds

The jovial Welsh spectator is referring to the Stone of Scone, used for centuries in the coronation of monarchs and seized during the English invasion of Scotland in 1296. In 1950, to draw attention to Scottish home rule, students stole it from Westminster Abbey. A few days before this cartoon appeared, the Stone was returned to London.

"When you've finished swearing at me about your blessed Stone I'll tell you I happen to be a Welshman."

Sunday Express, 15 April 1951

50 Bored and baffled UK-based GIs join the more traditional English spectators to watch a village cricket match.
Giles drew a number of cartoons featuring American servicemen, including the one opposite.

Holiday cricket

Sunday Express, 5 August 1951

Unlike those on the page opposite, the Americans from the local base have taken to cricket with enthusiasm but perhaps without entirely grasping the rules of the game. Around 45,000 American servicemen were stationed in Britain during the Cold War.

"Take it easy, Major, we've got them interested in the game – that's the thing."

Daily Express, 20 June 1952

52   British travel companies began promoting holidays abroad in the 1950s, but this one looks like it may not end well for the family. George Junior, trailing a toy bull, seems oblivious to the danger.

"The sooner this family learns that NO ENTRAD on a door in Spain means NO ENTRY the better."

Daily Express, 25 June 1953

For one of the twins the Highland Games at Braemar don't have the same appeal as the Farnborough Airshow, though Grandma, dancing a spritely Highland Fling, seems happy.

"I want to go to Farnborough Air Show!"

Sunday Express, 12 September 1954

Sponsored by the *Daily Express,* the UK's inaugural Boat Show, the first of its kind in the world, ran at London's Olympia Exhibition Centre from 30 December 1954 to 8 January 1955. Among the boats featured were a royal barge and a Royal Marines landing craft.

"Don't you 'hurry-for'ard-landlubber' me, you sea serpent."

Daily Express, 30 December 1954

"As that last smashing forehand drive lands in the far corner to bring him victory he leaps nimbly over the net to shake the hand of his opponent – Oh dear! His toe has just tipped the net..."

Daily Express, 26 June 1956

56 From the 1880s the Football League insisted on a minimum admission charge to football games to prevent price competition between clubs. It rose to a still-affordable one shilling ninepence in 1950. These football supporters, however, evidently have a dim view of the affordability of their tickets versus the benefits of the directors' tax loopholes.

"We'll have to lower their entrance price out of our tax relief – we're getting more 'Boos' than the ref..."

Daily Express, 11 April 1957

"Striking in sympathy with the bus drivers is one thing – refusing to make the tea is another."

Daily Express, 3 May 1958

58 The International Horse Show had been given the royal seal of approval two years previously and show jumping as a spectator sport increased dramatically in popularity over the next decade. It looks like Cold War hostilities had extended into the sporting arena here.

"Pater – what price Mamma's Anglo-Soviet relationship if the Russians walk away with it?"

Daily Express, 21 July 1959

The Wolfenden Committee's Report, published a few days earlier, had recommended the creation and funding – to the tune of five million pounds – of a Sports Development Council.

"Well, I'm certainly glad you brought me along to see what the Wolfenden Committee wants the taxpayer to subscribe £5,000,000 towards."

Sunday Express, 2 October 1960

A keen sailor, Giles regularly depicted the annual Boat Show at London's Earl's Court in his cartoons.

"It's real water, Dad. Grandma's blowing bubbles."

Daily Express, 6 January 1961

"The man who says he's going to sue the ref. for spoiling his afternoon's entertainment has started something – half of them have brought their solicitors and counsel."

Daily Express, 30 January 1962

Gentlemen v Players were first-class cricket matches held from 1806 to 1962 between amateur (Gentlemen) and professional (Players) cricketers.

"Football would sure have a problem if they had to do like cricket – sort out the Gentlemen and Players."

Daily Express, 29 November 1962

A disgruntled supporter is keen to offer the constables the goalkeeper for the police team. Another supporter has flung his rattle onto the field in disgust. Once common, football rattles were banned in the 1970s to prevent them being used as weapons by hooligans.

"He any good to you?"

Daily Express, 5 March 1964

64   Usually the first feature of the British flat racing on turf season, the Lincoln Handicap was run at Lincoln Racecourse for the last time in 1964 before it transferred to Doncaster. That year it was won by Mighty Ghurka, a 33/1 outsider.

"Hullo, Murgatroyd – what's your sick aunt you had the day off to visit backing in the next race?"

Daily Express, 17 March 1964

The Betting and Gaming Act of 1960 legalised casinos in Britain. About a thousand casinos were opened in the first five years, many of them a cover for criminal activity.

"Third one on the right's my boy – every time I take his 2s. 6d. he hisses 'Mafia!'"

Sunday Express, 26 February 1967

Evangelist Billy Graham, who had some controversial views about women, had returned to the UK on a campaign in June 1967.

"If we could leave the judgement on mini form to Billy Graham for a few moments..."

Daily Express, 20 June 1967

In 1968, the stringent dress code was relaxed a little to allow men to wear lounge suits in the Royal enclosure at Royal Ascot for the first time.

"Confounded cheek! Moscow students distributing leaflets demanding admission for Ascot women in trousers."

Daily Express, 20 June 1968

The day earlier, the Chancellor had announced in his Budget that he would cut purchase tax, increase pensions and raise personal allowances to put about £1 a week more in pay packets.

"So they've all got an extra pound in their pockets – well, I think we can do something about that."

Daily Express, 23 March 1972

A quintessentially English scene of Royal Ascot, rain and mild pessimism. It was the summer solstice and, as the gentleman points out, the days then start to become shorter.

"I simply remarked, mother, that after today the nights start drawing in."

Daily Express, 21 June 1973

70   At Wimbledon in 1973, fans of Swedish tennis idol Björn Borg were asked to keep calm. Extra stewards were called in after events the previous year, when hundreds of teenage girls had mobbed the young player every time he appeared. The plea for calm doesn't seem to have had any effect though, judging by this cartoon.

"Martha! Come back at once!"

Sunday Express, 1 July 1973

"You say 'Your Majesty' if you bump into the Queen. Not to Jean Rook."

Daily Express, 18 June 1974

The Wimbledon Championships had begun the previous day – 1975 saw perhaps one of the greatest Men's Singles finals, as Arthur Ashe beat Jimmy Connors to take his first Wimbledon title.

"There goes my 7 to 4 bet – according to that tic-tac man one of the players has belted a linesman before the game's started."

Daily Express, 24 June 1975

Formula One cars first began sporting tobacco company livery during the 1968 season and tobacco advertising was common in the sport.

"No 'thanks' I don't smoke."

Daily Express, 8 August 1975

The day after this cartoon appeared, England faced Italy in a crucial World Cup qualifying match at Stadio Olimpico in Rome. Italy went on to win 2–0.

"It's going to be a tough match, lads, they say the Italian riff-raff are riff-raffier than we are."

Daily Express, 16 November 1976

"But Prince Charles slid off to play polo before the end of the first race, Ma."

Daily Express, 19 June 1980

Despite Fred's jubilation, his wife is all too aware that bowling the chairman out for a duck is not the wisest career move.

"If I was your Fred with an appointment on Monday about his contract I wouldn't have clobbered the Chairman first ball."

Sunday Express, 16 August 1981

"I never want a drink when I go to football, it's after watching our lot play that I want one."

Sunday Express, 8 September 1985

It's hard to imagine anything further removed from hooliganism, scourge of English football throughout the 1980s, than the sartorial elegance and Champagne quaffing of Royal Ascot.

"So far hooliganism isn't identified with Ascot. But any more language like you've just used on your jockey and it'll be on the way."

Daily Express, 14 June 1988

Parties

Rock and roll has taken hold and, like many parents at the time, Father finds it something to be endured, not enjoyed.

"How come nobody in this house ever wants to elope?"

Daily Express, 16 July 1959

It wouldn't be the office Christmas party if at least one person didn't make a career-threatening faux pas.

"Pity if he heard you refer to him as a dreary misconception of an obsolete legend – that's the general manager."

Daily Express, 19 December 1961

The Cuban Missile Crisis, which brought the United States and Russia to the brink of war, had ended two days earlier, when Russian leader Nikita Khrushchev had announced that Soviet missiles would be removed from Cuba.

"I'll settle for it being a step towards world peace when we have a little less 'We sure put Khrushchev in his place.'"

Daily Express, 30 October 1962

82   The Profumo Affair, the 1960s scandal that helped topple the Conservative government, started when Secretary of State for War John Profumo began an affair with model Christine Keeler.

"Ladies and Gentlemen, Miss Chris –"

Daily Express, 11 June 1963

The Beatles had their first number one single, "Please Please Me", in February 1963 and by the end of the year Beatlemania had taken hold.

"I fear a lot of mummies and daddies are going to get L.P. Beatle records for Christmas."

Daily Express, 12 December 1963

84 "Auld Lang Syne" is traditionally sung at midnight on New Year's Eve to say goodbye to the old year. It was written by Scottish poet Robert Burns in 1788, based on a song that had been sung for centuries.

"Come in, Robbie Burns – we've only been waiting an hour and a half to sing Auld Lang Syne."

Sunday Express, 1 January 1967

"Faster everybody! Or we'll never get that Mini-Moke before the coupon ban."

One can only speculate about what comment had been made about the glamorous woman in the fur coat to elicit this response.

"No – as a matter of fact the one in the fur coat is my mother-in-law."

Daily Express, 28 November 1967

Grandma has pushed the boat out, as befits this smart wedding, and added a bargain pair of gloves to her signature black coat and fox stole.

"Bride's gown, flower-spattered tent of sheer white tulle from Liz Taylor's Paris Collection – Grandma's new gloves, white cotton, 3s. 11d., Alf's Bargain Store, High Street."

Daily Express, 23 January 1968

To mark America's bicentenary, Queen Elizabeth and Prince Philip visited the United States in 1976.

"You weren't supposed to curtsy, Elmer."

Sunday Express, 11 July 1976

In the 1970s, some believed that those on Social Security were better off than workers, though this gentleman is indignant
at the suggestion that his wealth may be government funded.

"I resent that remark, Harry! I do NOT do it all on the Social Security."

Daily Express, 15 July 1976

90   Ah, the joys of afternoon tea in the countryside. Giles once again demonstrates his skill in packing a cartoon with amusing detail.

"We'd like separate bills and 5% off for cash."

Sunday Express, 23 July 1978

"Which show did you say Bridget's new boyfriend would have been on but for the TV strike – Eurovision or the Muppets?"

Sunday Express, 11 March 1979

The chairman is clearly a man of few words and little Christmas cheer.

"Your Yuletide message to the office party last year, sir? Same as the year before – Merry Christmas, everybody. Over and out."

Daily Express, 20 December 1979

"Daddy's done it again – 'if they gave medals for peeling spuds he'd have been the most decorated ERK in Biggin Hill'."

Sunday Express, 14 September 1980

94 The previous evening England had beaten Paraguay 3–0 in the World Cup in Mexico. The quarter-final that took place between England and Argentina a few days later featured the legendary "hand of God" goal by Argentina's Diego Maradona.

"And now, Miss Smythe, perhaps we might commence dictation?"

Daily Express, 19 June 1986

Cricketer Ian Botham had just been recalled to the English Test match side, after serving a ban for smoking marijuana. Two days after this cartoon appeared, he went on to become the world's highest Test wicket taker.

"I wish Dad wouldn't be so pro-Botham in front of the children."

Daily Express, 19 August 1986

The Christmas revelry is about to be interrupted by Grandma's ire over her cut-price gift. Vera, put upon as always, is almost buckling under a tray of mince pies for the guests.

"Hold tight, Dad – someone's just found a pre-Christmas sale ticket on that bed jacket you gave her."

Sunday Express, 28 December 1986

"If the experts are right your daughter's marriage has a good chance of survival."

Daily Express, 10 May 1988

At the Pub

All together now: "Around the shores of England, which stretch towards the sea, there dwell an ancient people, and they labour mightily…" Father, enjoying both beer and song, on his Cornish holiday.

"Dad'll get 'Fishermen of England' when he arrives home two hours late." (St. Ives, Cornwall)

Daily Express, 24 August 1951

Flirting with GIs was probably not what Winston Churchill and Dwight D. Eisenhower had in mind as the special relationship between Britain and the United States.

"But, Bertie – I'm only doing it like Winston and Ike – encouraging Anglo-American relationship."

Sunday Express, 20 June 1954

100   There had been uproar in Parliament after Anthony Head, the Minister of Defence, reported bombing attacks by British aircraft and the sinking of an Egyptian frigate. Prime Minister Anthony Eden, asked whether a declaration of war had been made by the UK, replied that there had been no declaration of war but there was a state of armed conflict.

As Eden says, "This is not a state of war, simply armed conflict."

Sunday Express, 4 November 1956

"Dinger, is this bird calling us Squares?"

Sunday Express, 29 May 1960

The Common Agricultural Policy, which supported farmers in the Common Market, of which Britain was not yet a member, was launched in 1962.

"Can't you see 'em – Common Market all the morning, Folies-Bergere all the afternoon!"

Daily Express, 16 January 1962

The previous month, French President Charles de Gaulle had explicitly reiterated his opposition to the UK joining the European Common Market (see also the cartoon from 7 June 1962, on page 10).

"Agreed then – we send a note to de Gaulle telling him if he don't like Britain this club is cancelling its annual day-trip to Boulogne."

Sunday Express, 10 February 1963

104 The Arts Council was founded in 1946 to support all aspects of performing, visual and literary arts but very likely it might not view a bawdy ballad as "art".

"That last verse of yours not only mucked our chances of an Arts Council grant – it probably lost me my licence."

Daily Express, 19 October 1965

"Your Dad's banging away at Mr. Heath but it's really those new shoes that pinch a bit he's mad at."

Sunday Express, 20 March 1966

The 1966 general election was held on 31 March and was a landslide victory for Harold Wilson's Labour party.

"From what I've seen of our elders, if I was old enough to vote I wouldn't vote for anyone who was old enough to vote."

Daily Express, 31 March 1966

Newspapers reported that discussions were on-going with the Home Office as to whether 71-year-old Hollywood actor and prominent gambler George Raft should be allowed to re-enter the UK after a holiday in America.

"And to think we stop people coming into the country because they've got a few undesirable friends."

Daily Express, 28 February 1967

The 1960s saw British pubs becoming more family friendly as landlords sought to widen their customer base. This punter doesn't seem keen on the changes however.

"Two iced lollies and a packet of bubbly gum ruddy well isn't what I ordered."

Sunday Express, 13 August 1967

"Her best mild beer always did taste like OMO."

Sunday Express, 1 December 1968

110 Rogue policemen, especially those in the pay of gangsters, became a problem for the Metropolitan Police in the late 1960s. This member of London's finest appears to resent the implication that he may be one of them.

"Evening, Hamlet."

Ignacy Jan Paderewski (1860–1941) was a very popular Polish pianist and composer, who also served as the country's prime minister in 1919.

"It'll take more than her damn dog tricks and Paderewski on the joanna to get me out of the house tonight."

Sunday Express, 16 November 1969

This punter gets it 50 per cent right: the Belle of the Bar final at the Licensed Victualler's International Trade and Catering Exhibition on 26 April was indeed not won by "Raquel Welch", but by Wendy George. However Double Cream, rather than Friendly Way, won at Doncaster.

"8–1 Friendly Way, and 5–4 Raquel Welch here ain't in the first three of the Belle of the Bar contest."

Daily Express, 25 March 1971

"This is me Solicitor, me Junior Counsel and me Senior Counsel – now let's see what sort of change we get this time, yer thieving old trout."

Sunday Express, 12 October 1975

114   Giles took a light-hearted look at the Arts Council on more than one occasion (see also the cartoon from 19 October 1965, on page 104). This artwork was later displayed at the *Culture Cartooned* exhibition at the Beaney Museum in Canterbury in 2008.

"Methinks the boy Harry doth take the mock."

Sunday Express, 14 March 1976

Charlie's angry team-mates are making sure the hapless player is atoning for his sin.

115

"Morning Charlie. I hear thou didst commit a sin that passeth all understanding by thrice placing the ball in your own goal during the first match of the season."

Sunday Express, 20 August 1978

116   The second World Professional Darts Championship took place from 2 to 9 February in 1979. Also happening in early February was Crufts dog show, where Butch appears to have fared badly.

"Blame TV for more violence – making darts popular again!"

Sunday Express, 11 February 1979

The nation was two weeks into the lengthy ITV strike of 1979 and, like many others, Stinker and Ernie are forced to find alternative forms of entertainment.

"No ITV and BBC repeat repeats is driving us to drink."

Daily Express, 23 August 1979

118   US Secretary of State Alexander Haig had recently stated that NATO had a contingency plan "to fire a nuclear weapon for demonstrative purposes". The other Haig is Sir Douglas Haig, who led British forces at the 1916 Battle of the Somme.

"I suppose one could say you were a sort of demonstration missile when your Haig sent you to the Somme, Grandfather."

Sunday Express, 8 November 1981

The Home Service Force was formed in 1982, during the Cold War, as a type of Home Guard to defend key installations from enemy sabotage. Volunteers, of which there was no shortage, had to have previous armed forces experience.

"Ah, Kerridge, still wearing the old patriotic camouflage you wore on your midnight reconnoitres among my pheasants during the last lot?"

Sunday Express, 7 March 1982

Football violence was at its peak in the UK in the 1980s. Although Giles hated football hooliganism, he was a big fan of the sport.

"The boys say they're not going to waste their talents kicking people's heads in at football if they're not going to be on television."

Sunday Express, 27 February 1983

On Easter Monday 1983 armed robbers got into the Security Express depot in London, taking guards hostage and stealing almost £6 million, not £7 million as the caption says, in cash.

"I didn't say that our Charlie pushing the boat out means he's connected with the £7m robbery
– I simply said it makes him highly suspect."

Daily Express, 7 April 1983

In February 1984, Barney Curley raffled his Irish mansion, Middleton Park House, for £200 a ticket.
Nearly 9,000 hopefuls purchased tickets.

"Dad, can you spare a minute – Ernie raffled the house and a man's called to say he's won it."

Sunday Express, 12 February 1984

"Birdies, eagles, albatrosses – here's to the St. Andrews bird-watchers weekend."

Sunday Express, 22 July 1984

124   The hidden flavouring in his war-time tea is an unwelcome revelation for this former senior officer on Remembrance Sunday.

"We didn't have all this Cordon Bleu when I was your batman in the last lot – I used to boil your eggs in our 'ot tea."

Sunday Express, 11 November 1984

At Church

In early 1954 Senator Joseph McCarthy dramatically accused the United States Army of being "soft" on communism.

"Honey – this is a swell time to tell me that one of your aunties is a Commie."

Sunday Express, 7 March 1954

126 Giles was a keen supporter of Ipswich Town football team, featuring them often in his cartoons. The match the groom is referring to was against Torquay United, the Town losing 4–1.

"I hope he gets a move on – the Town kick-off at two-thirty and my ship sails at six."

Sunday Express, 19 August 1956

Soviet leader Nikita Khrushchev and US president Dwight D. Eisenhower were due to meet at Camp David in September of this year. Harold MacMillan was prime minister at the time.

"If the Summit talks fall through, calling him Dwight Nikita Harold is going to make him look pretty stupid."

Sunday Express, 30 August 1959

Rock star Adam Faith and the Archbishop of York, Donald Coggan, had appeared together on a BBC programme to debate religion.

"With all due respect to the Archbishop appearing on TV with Adam Faith – 'Someone Else's Baby' and the Twist are OUT."

Sunday Express, 28 January 1962

"I reckon Mr. Jones has got a cheek asking to have his sins forgiven after the way he played centre half yesterday."

Sunday Express, 23 August 1964

Naturally Grandma, with her forthright views, is among the enthusiastically disruptive "lot at the back".

"Because somebody said Christians should not detach themselves from politics does not entitle you lot at the back to keep chanting, 'What about the old age pension'."

Sunday Express, 11 October 1964

A few days earlier, *The Times* had reported that an inquiry had been ordered into severe gas restrictions caused by breakdowns at two West Midlands Gas Board plants.

"Best crowd we've had for months, thanks to gas and electricity cuts and my old coke heater."

Sunday Express, 23 January 1966

132 The day before this cartoon appeared, the Union of Post Office Workers voted in favour of an all-out strike in support of their pay claim. The Post Office denied reports by workers that they had been ordered to give pools coupons priority over other mail as the postal strike approached.

"I wouldn't fancy our striking postmistress's chances of having her trepasses forgiven if Vicar's pools don't reach their destinations on time."

Sunday Express, 17 January 1971

"I must have a word with the caretaker about this strange tapping noise in the vestry."

Sunday Express, 26 September 1971

134 Figures released the previous month had shown a large gap between the earnings of agricultural workers and other workers. The average weekly earnings of farm workers were £21.60 for a 47.9-hour week, compared to manual workers' £30.93 for a 44.7-hour week.

"And forgive us our trespasses and forgive me for wishing a plague upon Ernie Ragwart, my good and faithful farmworker who is demanding a 50% wage increase."

Sunday Express, 14 May 1972

"I would remind you that All Good Gifts Around Us have been carefully checked before the sermon."

Sunday Express, 1 October 1972

Three days earlier, the Church of England General Synod had agreed in principle to admit women to the priesthood.

"I must say a Reverend 36-24-36 wouldn't be a bad idea, eh Harry?"

Sunday Express, 6 July 1975

"Light reading during the sermon – 'Jaws' out, 'Linda Lovelace' in."

Sunday Express, 1 February 1976

The Drought Act came into force on 6 August 1976 as a result of that summer's heat wave.

"Oh Lord, forgive him, he knows not that he committeth an offence that doth carry a four hundred pound fine or one month, or both such penalties."

Daily Express, 19 August 1976

"They certainly do watch too much TV – this is the third one I've christened Starsky this week."

Bakery workers were on strike in September 1977, causing long queues and rationing of bread.

"In case anybody has any evil designs on our solitary loaf, curate will be riding shotgun, as it were."

Sunday Express, 11 September 1977

"Right – off skateboards everybody."

The hymn singing at the Sunday service is going to have to be very hearty to compete with the concert still going strong in the church hall.

"When I said if it was wet on Saturday they could use the Church Hall I didn't mean thro' Sunday."

Sunday Express, 4 September 1983

The long-awaited Sinclair TV80 pocket TV set was launched in September 1983. The choirboys like to adopt things en masse,
as can seen here and in the cartoons from 8 January 1978 and 26 September 1971, on pages 133 and 141.

"Right! Before the service – all new miniature televisions up sleeves on table!"

Sunday Express, 18 September 1983

In the 1980s, the EU's Common Agricultural Policy encouraged farmers to remove hedgerows by offering subsidies to make fields bigger.

"I think calling the farmers a conniving bunch of hedge and tree slashers in your first sermon was perhaps unfortunate."

Sunday Express, 30 September 1984

The greengrocer seems in little doubt as to those responsible for his generous – and unintended – contribution to the harvest festival.

"Hold it! Before we go in – Mr. Burrows complains that 6 marrows, 5lbs of tomatoes and 2 doz. cauliflowers are missing from his shop."

Sunday Express, 22 September 1985

February 1986 was bitterly cold with widespread snow throughout the month, cancelling many sporting fixtures.

"You ought to be ashamed! Betting the vicar 50–1 he couldn't get the course cleared at Wolverhampton in time for racing on Monday."

Sunday Express, 16 February 1986

Strikes & Demonstrations

On 17 September 1961, the Campaign for Nuclear Disarmament organised a mass sit-down demonstration in Trafalgar Square in protest at the arrival of Polaris missiles in the UK.

"If they tread on Grandma's toes many more times it'll be bang goodbye to the 'no violence either side' pact."

Sunday Express, 17 September 1961

On 28 April 1962, ten thousand nurses marched from Marble Arch to Trafalgar Square in a protest over wages.

"In case you've ideas about carrying 'em off 'Ban-the-Bomb' style, wifie's right behind you, Harry boy."

Sunday Express, 29 April 1962

The previous day, London Underground booking clerks went on strike to support their pay claim.

149

"For the record – during yesterday's booking clerks' strike 5,982 passengers used this station.
Net takings in the honesty box – one and ninepence."

Daily Express, 16 March 1965

150   It was not so jolly hockey sticks in January 1966 for prime minister Harold Wilson. He was dealing with a number of problems, including Rhodesia (now Zimbabwe), which had unilaterally declared independence from Britain two months earlier.

"Well, apart from a few items like Rhodesia, a gas crisis, a by-election, and a rail strike threat, I don't think he's doing much this morning."

Daily Express, 25 January 1966

There was severe shortage of nursery-school places in the 1960s. In 1968 a petition was presented to the House of Commons
seeking increased government funding for education for pre-school children.

"O.K.! That's enough of trying to control 'em with iced lollies. Draw batons!"

Daily Express, 21 May 1968

"Why are we sending you to negotiate with 'em? Because your missus is one of their ringleaders, that's why."

Daily Express, 30 May 1968

In 1972, Britain's railway unions were in dispute with British Rail over pay.
Eventually a settlement was reached and wages were increased by 13.5 per cent.

"And tell your mother to stop singing 'We'll meet again.' I might be back on the 5.30 in any case."

Daily Express, 12 May 1972

154 On 17 May 1972, school children attended a demonstration called by the Schools Action Union to protest corporal punishment and demand changes to the organisation of schools, including the reintroduction of free school milk.

"A fig for Pupil Power! At those wages a woman's privileged to change her mind."

Daily Express, 18 May 1972

Thousands of teenage girls had packed the roof gardens at Heathrow the previous day to greet the Osmonds, who were beginning their UK tour. Extra police were drafted in to help control the hysterical crowd.

"Music hath charms, Charlie boy."

Daily Express, 23 October 1973

On 22 April 1974, car workers' wives and children marched to the British Leyland plant at Cowley to protest against strike leaders, whom they blamed for keeping the men from working.

"Listen, mate, a whack from my missus is one thing – but one from yours is another."

Daily Express, 25 April 1974

Power cuts were a common occurrence in the 1970s, affecting TV broadcasting including beloved comedy puppet show *The Muppet Show*, clearly popular with these coalminers too.

"Agreed 100 per cent! We ask our brothers in the power stations not to have electricity cuts during *The Muppet Show*."

Daily Express, 2 November 1977

In 1988 nurses took unprecedented industrial action, an opportunity these patients have seized upon as a chance to escape to the pub.

"Just turn your back for a few hours strike and they're off."

Sunday Express, 10 January 1988

"While you've still got some left it's your shout."

Sunday Express, 28 October 1990

British Cartoon Archive

All the cartoons in this book were copied from material in Carl Giles's own private archive, a huge collection of artwork, ephemera and correspondence, which is held by the British Cartoon Archive at the University of Kent. Carl Giles had been cartoonist for Lord Beaverbrook's *Daily* and *Sunday Express* for almost 20 years, when on 20 March 1962 the Conservative M.P. Sir Martin Lindsay tabled a motion deploring "the conduct of Lord Beaverbrook in authorizing over the last few years in the newspapers controlled by him more than 70 adverse comments on members of the royal family who have no means of replying."

Lindsay was wrong about the royal family having no means of reply. That day Prince Philip also vented his anger at Beaverbrook's campaign, during a press reception at the British Embassy in Rio de Janeiro. According to the paper's Brazil representative, the Prince declared that, "The *Daily Express* is a bloody awful newspaper. It is full of lies, scandal and imagination. It is a vicious paper."

When the *Daily Express* reported this the next day, Giles decided to treat it as a joke. He knew the royal family enjoyed his cartoons; they often asked for the artwork. This had begun in 1948, when Prince Philip was sent a cartoon on the State Opening of Parliament, and over the next few years Giles received a steady stream of requests from Buckingham Palace for original drawings.

Giles drew the diminutive Lord Beaverbrook being escorted through the Traitor's Gate at the Tower of London, with a headsman's axe and block standing ready in the background. The caption repeated Prince Philip's condemnation of the *Daily Express*, but added laconically: "'Ah well,' said Lord B., as they trotted him off to the Tower, 'at least he takes it or he wouldn't know it was a bloody awful newspaper.'"

This was a brilliant response, which did much to defuse the situation. When Giles's cartoon was printed the next day, *Daily Express* staff were surprised to receive a phone call from Queen Elizabeth II's press secretary, with a message for Giles that "Her Majesty requests today's cartoon to commemorate one of her husband's most glorious indiscretions."

Giles sent off the artwork and in May 1962 found himself invited to "a small informal luncheon party" at Buckingham Palace with Queen Elizabeth II and Prince Philip, Duke of Edinburgh. "I was filled with absolute dread," Giles recalled afterwards. "But as soon as she started to talk I was put at my ease…There were about half a dozen corgis running about in a completely uncontrolled state. Suddenly the Queen shouted, 'HEP'. It was like a bark from a sergeant major. The corgis immediately stood to attention. Then filed out of the room."

After the lunch Giles mischievously drew a cartoon of the guests leaving with corgi-savaged trousers. He sent it to the Queen, who returned her thanks through one of her private secretaries, noting that she was "glad that you got away without having lost, at least to the best of her knowledge, so much as a shred of your trousers".

After that Giles became what one *Daily Express* journalist called "a kind of cartooning jester to the royal family". By the time he retired in 1991, the royal family had more than 40 of his original drawings, the largest number being owned by Prince Philip, who shared Giles's anarchic view of the world.

The British Cartoon Archive, based at the University of Kent's Templeman Library in Canterbury, is dedicated to the history of British cartooning over the last two hundred years. It holds the artwork for more than 150,000 British political and social-comment cartoons, plus large collections of comic strips, newspaper cuttings, books and magazines. Its website at www.cartoons.ac.uk has over 200,000 cartoon images, including the majority of Carl Giles's published work.

Left: *Lord Beaverbrook is marched to the Tower, 22 March 1962.*